Other books by Howard Cruse:

Wendel
Dancin' Nekkid with the Angels

Wendel on the Rebound

by **Howard Cruse**

St. Martin's Press
New York

ACKNOWLEDGMENTS:

I would like to offer thanks to Robert I. McQueen, formerly the editor-in-chief of *The Advocate*, for inviting me to create *Wendel* for that magazine, and to Lenny Giteck, Mark Thompson, Michael Shively, and the current executive editor, Stuart Kellogg, each of whom has had a hand in keeping the strip alive.

I'm grateful to Michael Denneny, my editor at St. Martin's Press, for shepherding both this and my previous cartoon book, *Dancin' Nekkid with the Angels*, into print, and to my agent, Athos Demetriou, for his role in making *Wendel on the Rebound* happen.

I'd like to thank Sacramento photographer Eileen Hyland for allowing me to use her photograph of the NAMES Project Memorial Quilt, taken during the National March on Washington for Lesbian and Gay Rights in 1987.

Finally, I'm grateful to my lover, Ed Sedarbaum, not only for encouraging me during my many writer's blocks and deadline panics but also for contributing his professional copyediting skills. Any grammatical errors that remain in the following comic strips are there because I stubbornly refused to follow his counsel, citing either artistic license or the Cruse Theory of Alternative Linguistics.

Library of Congress Cataloging-in-Publication Data

Cruse, Howard.
    Wendel on the rebound / Howard Cruse.
       p.   cm.
    ISBN 0-312-03002-9
    1. Gay men—Comic books, strips, etc. I. Title.
PN6727.C74W46 1989
741.5'973—dc19
                                         89-4051
                                          CIP

First Edition
10 9 8 7 6 5 4 3 2 1

Dedication:

To everyone who was there or who would have been if they could.

Photo: Eileen Hyland

A Note from the Cartoonist

September 1988

When last spotted between the covers of a book (*Wendel*, 1985), Wendel Trupstock and Ollie Chalmers had finally, after a long courtship, moved in together, determined to make a serious go of their gay couplehood.

But just as the young lovers stood poised to face their future in tandem, their cartoon universe suffered a fateful jolt. *The Advocate*, the gay newsmagazine that had always been home to Wendel, underwent a number of design changes, including a reduction in the size of its pages. The new *Advocate*, alas, could no longer accommodate the unusual, oversized format of the early *Wendel* strips.

Undrawn and consequently invisible, Wendel and his friends spent many months adrift in whatever void displaced cartoon characters characteristically drift in.

But now, lo and behold, Wendel is back! Actually, he's *been* back in *The Advocate* since late 1986, when that magazine generously offered the gang more space than ever before to have their adventures in: two full pages in each biweekly issue.

And now here those *Advocate* strips are in a book—along with two brand-new installments that even the *Advocate*'s readers never saw.

Believe me, it felt great to pick up my pen, take a deep breath, and resume drawing all of those old familiar faces again....

Here's our hero, Wendel Trupstock!

For now Wendel's stuck in the mail room at **Effluvia magazine**, but a great *science-fiction novel* simmers within him, right under breakfast!

Ollie
Chalmers...

Wendel's lover! He runs
a mean **photocopying
machine** at the **Quik-Zip
Copy Shop** while dreaming
of a life in the **theatre!**

Sterno...

Ollie's childhood chum and a bold roving photographer for **Gayblaze**, the local gay newspaper! Sterno's journalistic rallying cry is: *MORE NEWS ABOUT NAKED MEN!!*

Deb Laurel...

An assistant editor at **Effluvia!** Though customarily demure, Deb once bribed a gym attendant **fifty bucks** to let her smell **Martina Navratilova's tennis shoes** after a **tournament!**

Vern & Myrtle Trupstock...

Wendel's dad & mom! Give Myrt a **liberation movement** and she'll bake **apple pies** for it!

Tina...

Deb's steamy girlfriend! A randomly abrasive and drug-warped loudmouth, Tina views her **sociopathic traits** as **tools** for **human liberation** rather than as ends in **themselves!**

Famous crimefighters
Branman & Clawboy...

(Cloaked in perpetual mystery, their secret identities are **Farley Chalmers**—that's Ollie's son—and his faithful feline companion...uh...

Clawboy!)

Ollie's ex-wife
Carol...

No picture available, but you may have caught her **silhouette** on **'Donahue'**...

...AND THEN MY HUSBAND TOLD ME HE WAS A ⸳sob!⸳ **HOMOSEXUAL!**...

HELLO—IS THIS THE PROPRIETOR OF THE **QUIK-ZIP COPY SHOP** ON **BRANCH STREET**?

THIS IS THE REVEREND **PAT ROBERTSON** HERE!

THAT'S **RIGHT!** I'M THE HOTSHOT **EVANGELIST** THAT'S CONTEMPLATING A RUN FOR THE **PRESIDENCY** SOON!

MM-HMM!

NOW YOU CAN JUST **IMAGINE** HOW MANY **MILLIONS** OF **BUCKS** I'M GONNA BE DROPPING ON SOME INDUSTRIOUS **COPY SHOP** LIKE **YOURS**...

...WHAT WITH **POSTERS!**

FLYERS!

FUND-RAISING MAIL!

I'M GONNA BE BLOWING **MONEY** OUT THE **HOLY WAZOO!**

HOW**EVER...**

SLAM!

...I **DON'T** WANT MY CAMPAIGN LITERATURE **CONTAMINATED** BY ANY **SATANIC, HEDONISTIC, HUMANISTIC TENDENCIES** ON THE PART OF MY **COPY SHOPS!**

DO YOU **GET** WHAT I'M **SAYIN'**, SPORT?

ANY COPY SHOP THAT WORKS FOR **ME** HAS GOT TO BE A **RIGHT-THINKING, ANTI-COMMUNIST, CHRISTIAN, FREEDOM-LOVING, BIBLE-READING, OLD-FASHIONED, FAMILY-ORIENTED ESTABLISHMENT!**

ARE YOU **READIN'** ME?

AM I **SAFE** IN ASSUMING THAT **YOUR** COPY SHOP FILLS THE BILL?

...OR AM I BARKING UP THE WRONG **TREE?**

...FIVE... FOUR... THREE... TWO... ONE...

WELL, AS A MATTER OF FACT, JUST **TODAY** WE ROOTED OUT A **HOMOSEXUAL** WHO'S BEEN ON THE PAYROLL FOR SOME **TIME!** YOU CAN BET WE SENT **HIM** PACKING BEFORE HE KNEW WHICH END WAS **UP!**

THA·A·AT'S RIGHT...SLIP RIGHT INTO OUR **HANDS**, FOOLISH EARTHLING!

...EXCUSE ME, I HAVE TO GET OFF THE **PHONE** NOW! A COUPLE OF THOUSAND PEOPLE HAVE JUST COME IN AND STARTED **PELTING** ME WITH **USED CONDOMS!**

CRUSE

Wendel by Howard Cruse

WENDEL AND DEB ARE **OLD HANDS** AT NEGOTIATING THE **TIDES** AND **UNDERTOWS** OF THE **LESBIAN & GAY IDEOLOGICAL SOLIDARITY COMMITTEE**...

...**B**UT IT'S A **BRAND NEW GAME** FOR DEB'S LOVER, TINA...

You're being sex-negative!

You're being patriarchal!

You're giving aid and comfort to the war machine!

I move that we table the decision on whether to order glazed or cream-filled donuts pending a detailed political re-analysis!

I object! Parliamentary Procedure is reactionary!

belch!

No decisions without concensus!

Are you feeling O.K., Tina?

FEB. 14 GAY & LESBIAN VALENTINE'S DAY SOCK ♥ HOP ♥

I'LL LIVE! BUT THESE **POLITICAL MEETINGS** YOU AND DEB DRAG ME TO DRIVE ME OUTA MY **GOURD!**

© 1987 by H. Cruse

WHY DON'T YOU TURKEYS DECIDE TO DYNAMITE **EDWIN MEESE'S DILDO COLLECTION** OR SOMETHING? **THAT** I COULD GET **INTO!**

TINA'S **EDGY!**

SHE'S PISSED THAT ALL THIS **FOLDEROL** COULD MAKE HER **LATE** FOR THE **ROCKY HORROR PICTURE SHOW!**

BELIEVE ME, TINA—WENDEL AND I ARE TRYING TO **HURRY** ALL OF THIS **ALONG!**

Now we need somebody to organize the Spring fund-raiser...

Y'HEAR **THAT,** SUCKER? YOU KNOW WHAT **THAT** MEANS, DON'T YOU?

NO **NO NO,** MUTTONCHOP! NOT **THIS TIME!** THIS TIME I'M GONNA BE **FIRM!**

SO **WHICH ONE** OF YOU HIGHLY CAPABLE GUYS 'N' GALS FEELS LIKE SPEARHEADING OUR **FUNDRAISING DRIVE?**

Uh... You're pretty good at that kind of thing, Deb...

STOP WHERE YOU ARE, FRIEND! JUST NIP THAT THOUGHT IN THE BUD!

I'M ALWAYS THE ONE WHO VOLUNTEERS FOR EVERYTHING! THIS CAN'T GO ON!

DO YOU HEAR WHAT I'M SAYING? I'M APPROACHING BURNOUT!!

BOP!

I'VE GOT A PERSONAL LIFE —Y'KNOW? I DON'T OWE THE GAY MOVEMENT EVERY MINUTE OF EVERY DAY!

FEB GAY & VALE DAY H

YOU PEOPLE HAVE GOTTA BE WILLING TO CARRY YOUR WEIGHT!

YOU MAY THINK I'M KIDDING, BUT IF SOMEBODY ELSE IN THIS ROOM DOESN'T VOLUNTEER, THE JOB IS JUST NOT GOING TO GET DONE!

I'VE REACHED MY LIMIT! I'M NOT GONNA BAIL YOU OUT THIS TIME!

DON'T EXPECT ME TO BACK DOWN THE WAY I'VE DONE BEFORE!

I'M SORRY, BUT THAT'S JUST THE WAY IT IS!

SHE'LL DO IT IF YOU BEG!

Ple·e·ease, Deb...

We nee-e-ed you! You've gotta help us!

Nobody does it like you do!

Please! Please! Please! Please! Please!

TINA! WAS THAT ETHICAL??

ARE YOU KIDDIN', STRAWHEAD? I SHOULD GET A MEDAL!

OH... ALL RIGHT, YOU GUYS...

...I JUST KNOCKED A GOOD FIFTEEN MINUTES OF BULLSHIT OFF OF GAY LIBERATION'S MARCH TO VICTORY

CRUSE

Wendel

by Howard Cruse

AND DON'T READ OVER MY SHOULDER!

WRITING ANOTHER LETTER TO YOUR GAY UNCLE IN THE BIG CITY?

YEP!

Tap Tap Tap

MY LETTERS TO UNCLE LUKE HAVE ALWAYS BEEN JUST BETWEEN HIM AND ME!

Dear Uncle Luke,

Things are going great for Ollie and me. We're very happy.

The only thing is that I don't know where I'm going with my life.

This way

This way

My mail room job at Effluvia doesn't show a lot of promise.

SHOULD WE DO DELOREAN?

WE'VE ALREADY DONE DELOREAN!

I want to be a great writer, but I can't think of anything great to write.

©1987 by H. Cruse

Mom thinks I write space stories because I'm afraid of the complications of life on Earth.

IT'S SAPPING MY WILL! Gulp! IT'S TRYING TO TRANSFORM ME INTO AN EVIL MINION OF GLOXTAR!

I get the feeling that Ollie thinks that, too.

IT'S GOOD, WENDEL! IT'S GOT...UH... LOTS OF ACTION!

He loves me, but when we argue he starts treating me like a kid.

I USED TO SAY THE SAME THING WHEN I WAS YOUR AGE...

IT ALL SPRINGS FROM A TRAUMATIC **FLING** I ONCE HAD WITH A **MARINE CORPS** RECRUITER I CRUISED AT **SAN FRANCISCO INTERNATIONAL**!

TAKE MY WORD FOR IT, NEPHEW—EVEN THE MOST **IDYLLIC** OF INFATUATIONS ISN'T WORTH **THREE TORTUROUS YEARS** OF ENFORCED **GOOD HEALTH** AND **FITNESS**!

South Northway 15
North Southway 18

YOU SHOULD **TELL** WENDEL THE WHOLE STORY OF YOUR **MILITARY CAREER** SOMETIME, LUKE!

I'M ALL **EARS**!

WHAT? AND SHAKE THE BOY'S **FAITH** IN OUR **NATIONAL DEFENSE**?

AFTER ALL, IT **STARTED OFF** RATHER **LYRICALLY**! IT WAS ONLY AT THE **END** THAT IT TURNED **LOATHSOME**!

...AS IS SO **OFTEN** THE CASE IN LIFE'S JOURNEYS!

I'M SURE CLARK'S AND MY **RELATIONSHIP** WILL SUFFER THE **SAME FATE**! ANY **DECADE** NOW, THE **ROSY GLOW** WILL BEGIN TO **FADE**!

HOW **TRUE**! I ALMOST **LOOK FORWARD** TO THE SWEET **TRAGEDY** OF IT ALL!

BUT WHAT ABOUT **YOU**, WENDEL? WHAT NOTEWORTHY PHOBIAS DO **YOU** HARBOR?

YES... WHAT'S YOUR **DEEPEST** AND MOST **INCAPACITATING FEAR**?

TAXI

BEING **FOUND OUT**!

UH...

WHAT I MEANT TO SAY WAS: BEING **LEFT** OUT!... ...STANDING ON THE **SIDELINES** ALL MY LIFE AND WATCHING THE WORLD GO BY **WITHOUT** ME!

I DON'T THINK YOU NEED TO FEAR **THAT**!

ANYONE WITH YOUR **ENERGY, PLUCK,** AND **YOUTHFUL BUNS** WILL HAVE THE WORLD **NIPPING** AT YOUR **HEELS**

YOU CAN COUNT ON THE **MARINE CORPS** AND THE **MOONIES** TO PUT IN FERVENT BIDS AT THE VERY **LEAST**!

CRUSE

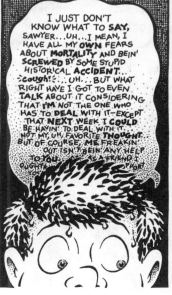

Wendel

by Howard Cruse

WENDEL'S ON HIS WAY HOME, AND THERE'S TIME TO THINK...

WOULD YOU LIKE ME TO TAKE THAT CUP, SIR?

THANKS!

SIGH... EXCUSE ME, MA'AM...

I HATE TO BOTHER YOU, BUT WOULD IT BE POSSIBLE TO OPEN THE AIRPLANE DOOR A CRACK FOR JUST A MINUTE?

YOU ARE KIDDING, AREN'T YOU? THE WHOLE CABIN WOULD DE-PRESSURIZE, FOR STARTERS...

OH! I GUESS IT WOULD, WOULDN'T IT?

THEN YOU PROBABLY CAN'T OPEN UP ANY OF THOSE LITTLE WINDOWS ON THE SIDE, EITHER..?

Y'SEE, I'D REALLY LIKE TO TOSS THIS UNFINISHED NOVEL I'VE BEEN WRITING OUT OF THE PLANE WHILE WE'RE FLYING! IT'D HAVE A DEFINITE CLEANSING EFFECT ON MY SOUL...

READ MY LIPS, SIR: NO!!

©1987 by H. Cruse

YOU CAN DISPOSE OF YOUR BOOK EASILY AFTER WE LAND!

OF COURSE I CAN! HEH HEH... SILLY ME!

HOW FRUSTRATING! CHUCKING IT IN A DUMB AIRPORT WASTE BASKET ISN'T VERY FULFILLING!

I DON'T SUPPOSE YOU HAVE A CIGARETTE LIGHTER ON YOU..?

...AND DON'T EVEN THINK ABOUT BURNING IT!!

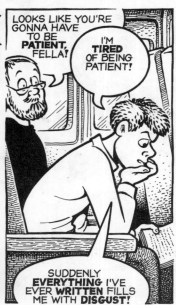

LOOKS LIKE YOU'RE GONNA HAVE TO BE PATIENT, FELLA!

I'M TIRED OF BEING PATIENT!

SUDDENLY EVERYTHING I'VE EVER WRITTEN FILLS ME WITH DISGUST!

'THE MARTIAN WORE REEBOKS!' CUTE TITLE!

IT'S JUVENILE TRIPE!

I BROUGHT IT WITH ME TO SHOW TO MY UNCLE...

...BUT I ENDED UP TOO EMBARRASSED TO EVEN MENTION IT TO HIM!

IT'S GOT NOTHING TO DO WITH LIFE OR DEATH OR COURAGE OR ANYTHING IMPORTANT!

I DON'T KNOW HOW I COULD'VE BEEN SO STUPID AS TO EVEN PUT IT ON PAPER!

HAS ANYBODY IN THIS PLANE GOT A PAPER-SHREDDER??

CALM DOWN, SON! WHY DON'T YOU GIVE THAT TO ME?

?

GO AHEAD! POP IT INTO MY ATTACHE CASE!

...JUST THINK OF IT AS A BOTTOMLESS PIT!

BASED ON EXPERIENCE, I CAN GUARANTEE THAT PRACTICALLY EVERY MANUSCRIPT THAT'S IN IT IS DESTINED FOR OBLIVION!

UH... WAIT A MINUTE...

HERE'S MY CARD... IT'LL SAVE A LOT OF EXPLAINING!

MOST OF OUR HARDCOVERS ARE NON-FICTION, BUT WE DO HAVE A SOFTCOVER S.F./FANTASY LINE!

GEE WHIZ!

WOULD I GET AN ADVANCE? DO YOU SELL MOVIE RIGHTS?

AAARGH... WHAT AM I SAYING?!

Bonk! Bonk!

I SEE YOUR NAME AND ADDRESS ARE HERE WHERE THEY SHOULD BE! I'LL BE IN TOUCH WITH YOU ONE WAY OR THE OTHER...

I FEEL SERIOUSLY COMPROMISED... I REALLY INTENDED TO DESTROY THAT MANUSCRIPT!

I PROMISE I'LL SPILL COFFEE ON ALL THE PAGES! YOU'LL NEVER BE ABLE TO SUBMIT IT AGAIN!

CRUST

NEXT ISSUE: BACK TO THE REAL WORLD!

WELL, LET'S SEE... IT'S **MURDER** ON MY **FEET**... I'VE GAINED **THREE POUNDS** FROM THE **NIBBLING**...

...AND I'M HAVING TROUBLE RECALLING WHAT MADE ME THINK IT WAS GONNA HELP ADVANCE MY **ACTING CAREER!**

I'M HAVING SOME DOUBTS ABOUT MY JOB AT **EFFLUVIA MAGAZINE,** TOO! IT SEEMS KINDA **IRRELEVANT!**

ALL CELEBRITY GOSSIP IS IRRELEVANT... EXCEPT WHEN IT'S ABOUT **ME!**

REMEMBER I'VE TOLD YOU ABOUT MY OLD BOYFRIEND **SAWYER?** I VISITED HIM IN THE CITY! HE'S GOT **AIDS!**

OH, JESUS, BABE!...

THINGS ARE SCREWED UP ON EVERY **SIDE,** WENDEL! AND THERE'S A DAMN **ELECTION** COMING UP! GAYS HAVE GOTTA GET **MOBILIZED!**

Aaaarrggh...

IT MAKES MY **HEAD** SPIN **THINKIN'** ABOUT IT!

AND Y'KNOW WHAT'S **CRAZY?**

RIGHT NOW IT'S HARD TO BELIEVE WE HAVE ANY PROBLEMS AT **ALL!**

I **KNOW** WHAT YOU **MEAN!**

NATURE'S DOING ALL THE **WORK** FOR US!

THE PLANET JUST **SPINS ALONG** THROUGH **SPACE** WITHOUT ANY HELP FROM THE **PASSENGERS!**

THE **TREE BRANCHES** ARE DOIN' A **SLOW DANCE** FOR US... THE **SKY** IS THOROUGHLY STOCKED WITH **STARS...**

THAT **BREEZE** FEELS REALLY **GREAT** ON MY **SKIN...**

THE **RUBBERS,** WE HAD TO GET FROM A **PHARMACY,** BUT ASIDE FROM **THAT—**

YEAH... EVERYTHING IS **PROVIDED!**

© 1988 by H. Cruse

"I DIDN'T PAY A LOT OF **ATTENTION** TO OTIS ONCE I'D GOTTEN ACCEPTED BY THE CROWD MY **AGE!**"

"LATER IT HIT ME THAT I **NEVER** HEARD HIM SAY THE WORDS '**GAY**' OR '**HOMOSEXUAL**!' HE ACTED AS IF HE HAD NO IDEA **WHO** HE WAS **PARTYING WITH** AT ALL THESE GET-TOGETHERS!"

I DON'T THINK OTIS EVER ACTUALLY HAD **SEX** WITH ANYBODY!

RALPH, ARE YOU AN' GEORGE GONNA 'GET **SILLY**' AGAIN TONIGHT TH' WAY YOU DID **LAST** WEEK?

OH, YOU NEVER CAN TELL **WHAT** GEORGE AN' I MIGHT WIND UP DOIN', OTIS...

"I'D SEE HIM AND SAY **HELLO**, OF COURSE! HE ALWAYS SEEMED HAPPY TO SEE ME HAVING **FUN!**"

WELL, COME TO **THINK** OF IT, I GUESS HE **MUST** HAVE!

...BUT YOU'D NEVER **KNOW** IT FROM SEEING HIM AT THOSE **PARTIES** —OR EVEN AT THE **TEAROOM!**

"AS TEAROOM COME-ONS GO, FLASHING AN OLD **McGOVERN** BUTTON ISN'T EXACTLY YOUR MOST **DIRECT** ROUTE TO A **SCORE!**"

"McGOVERN SHRIVER IN '72"

"MY LAST WEEKEND IN MONTANA, SOME OF THE PARTY GANG THREW ME A **FAREWELL BASH** WITH A **CAKE** AND ALL! OTIS WAS SITTING BESIDE ME AT A TABLE WITH A BUNCH OF OTHERS, AND HE REACHED OVER AND GRABBED ONTO MY **HAND!**"

"HE HELD ONTO MY HAND FOR A GOOD **HALF HOUR**, I GUESS...STARING INTO SPACE, NEVER EVEN **GLANCING** AT ME..."

"HE DIDN'T SAY ANYTHING! **I** COULDN'T THINK OF ANYTHING TO SAY, **EITHER!**"

"THE OTHERS AT THE TABLE JUST JOKED AMONG THEMSELVES AND IGNORED WHAT WAS GOING ON!"

"FINALLY HE TURNED LOOSE..."

CRUSE

...SO **I** WILL!

"PEOPLE HAVE TOLD ME THAT, AS THE YEARS WENT BY, OTIS'S **DRINKING** GOT SO **OUT OF CONTROL** THAT EVERYBODY GOT SICK OF **DEALING** WITH HIM!"

CHRIST ALMIGHTY, OTIS! I **TOLD** YOU YOU WERE GONNA **BREAK** THAT THING!

OOPS!

SMASH!

"WHEN HE GOT **DIAGNOSED**, HIS **AUNT** LET HIM COME LIVE WITH HER IN **IDAHO!**"

"FROM WHAT I HEAR, HE DIED A **YEAR** OR SO AGO!"

THE WAY THINGS WENT, I DOUBT THAT ANYBODY'S **THOUGHT** TO SEW A PANEL FOR OTIS...

About the Cartoonist

Howard Cruse was born and raised in Alabama.

In the early seventies he was the art director for a small television station in Birmingham, where he also provided the voices of Wilbur the Groundhog and Oscar the Yellow Monkey on the station's live afternoon TV kiddie show.

In the years since then he has contributed hundreds of pages to underground comic books, and was the founding editor of *Gay Comix*, launched in 1980.

For nine years he and his lover Ed Sedarbaum, a freelance book editor, have made their home in New York City. Ed was the original inspiration for Sterno, though he asserts that recently he has been feeling more like Tina.